For all our bairnies
In loving memory of JWC
For my darling wee Doodle

First published in Scotland in 2018

IBSN 9781999926502

Text copyright © Alison Page
Illustrations copyright © Kirsty Oxley

This book belongs to

_____

Corrie's Capers

The
Westie Fest

ILLUSTRATED BY
KIRSTY OXLEY

WRITTEN BY
ALISON PAGE

Corrie is a wonderful wee
West Highland Terrier.

Lochranza

Corrie

THE ISLE
OF
ARRAN

Brodick

Machrie

Lamlash

Holy Isle

Blackwaterfoot

Whiting Bay

Lagg

She is named after
one of the villages on
the Isle of Arran,
in Scotland.

She walks with a
hippety-skip
and welcomes everyone
she meets with
a wag of her tail.

But Corrie isn't quite like other dogs…

When Corrie hears
"Walkies!"
she runs to her bed,
props her chin
on the pillow
and pretends to
be fast asleep.

Could Corrie be a teensy-weensy bit lazy?

Corrie enjoys spending time with her Papa, Curaidh. Curaidh is a Gaelic word, pronounced *coo-ray*, which means hero or champion.

Although Papa is old and slowing down now, he tells Corrie that once upon a time he was very fit and a champion at the Westie Fest Games.

The Games are to be held on Arran again,
and Papa is sad he is too old to compete.

Corrie wants her Papa to be happy. Instead of lying around in her comfy bed, she is going to surprise everyone by getting fit enough to take part in the Westie Fest Games.

Hmm, there is a lot more to being a champion than she first thought! Corrie needs some help with her training if she is going to be selected for the Scottish team. She knows just the person…

Corrie waits patiently at the pier for the ferry to arrive into Brodick with all the visitors to the Arran Westie Fest.

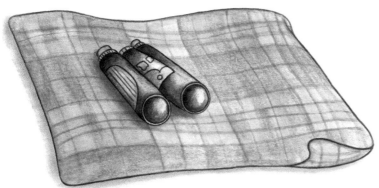

She offers them a warm
waggy-tail
welcome.

The Westies are treated to a lovely tour of the island.

There are lots of interesting things to see and do on the Isle of Arran.

A terrific trip round the Isle of Arran Distillery includes a nip…

...but not the biting kind! Cheers!

The Westies finish their sightseeing in Lamlash
where the Games have been set up on the village green.

The church bells ring out and the Games begin
with the Highland fling.

Thorfinn from Norway is a bit wobbly tossing the caber.

Ooof-a-woof… "Look out behind you!"

The Scottish team performs well.

Hamish hurls the haggis balls.
Oh yes, he looks like a winner… but, oh dear!
"You're not supposed to eat them, Mac!"

Meg and Rosa swim out strongly in front in the Lamlash Splish-Splash. "Keep going, girls. Don't slow down!"

The Lamlash Dash is over in a flash.

The tug of war team looks a bit on the light side.
"Heave-ho! You need to dig in!"

The Pipe Band plays some *grrre*at toe-tapping tunes.

Corrie can hear the crowd cheering for her as she warms up.
She has three chances in the triple jump.

On her first jump, the judge holds up a red flag.
Uh-oh, Corrie's paw has crossed the white line, so it doesn't count.

On her second jump, the crowd roars so loudly
that Corrie misses the whistle to start.
She rushes forwards, mixes up her hop-and-skip timings
and ends up running through the sand.

Dearie me, things aren't going at all well.
And to make matters worse,
black clouds are hovering overhead.

Two big raindrops
plop onto Corrie's face.
Will the grass be slippery?
Will she fall?

Corrie takes a deep breath.
She turns slowly and lines up for her third and final jump.
The whistle blows and the noisy crowd falls silent.

Papa watches nervously
from the sidelines.

Ready, steady… GO!

Skippety…   hippety…

hip-hip-hip...   hop.

WOW! It definitely looks like a BIG jump.

No red flag this time but what does it measure?

Is it enough?

The judge nods. *Yesss!* The crowd erupts. Corrie wins gold!
The medal ceremony finishes off a fantastic Games.

The Westies head back over the hill to Brodick,
streamers flying and smiles all round.

The Arran Pipe Band leads the Westies in a parade
along the front towards the pier.

Homeward bound, the Westies leave the island with their Arran doggy bags. What a wonderful Westie Fest! Three cheers for Corrie!

"Haste ye back," barks Corrie as she waves them off.

Corrie meets up with all her best pals
and shows them her gold medal.

She celebrates with a HUGE mouth-watering steak pie from the Arran butcher and her favourite ice cream for pudding – braw!

Corrie is delighted to see her Papa so happy. Without his help, she would never have won a medal. He will always be her hero.

Corrie's not lazy; she's an Arran Westie Fest champion who loves her Papa… and her comfy bed.

Z Z Z Z

Time for a
snooze!

Oh, Corrie, dear Corrie
you're my darling wee Westie;
I love you so much,
you're my absolute bestie.
Each day we go "walkies"
and off we do trot;
whether hail, rain or shine,
it doesn't matter a jot.
Corrie Doodle, wee Doodle,
in your kit and caboodle,
with a skippety-hippety step,
hip-hip-hip-hop.

Alison's Acknowledgements

Dear John and Alexander,
Thank you for your love, patience and encouragement.
I couldn't have done this without you.

With special thanks to:
Kirsty Oxley for her amazing artistic talent.
Lynne and Sandra Macvicar for kind permission to recycle the family name given to the Corrie/Sannox annual festival of fun and games.
The Isle of Arran Pipe Band and Mogabout Arran Safari for agreeing to be "Westified".
Kirsty Luke for listening, believing in me and sharing her network.
Diana Devlin and Patricia Trewby for their interest, help and support.
Alan Durant and Judith Paskin for their editorial guidance and sound professional advice.
June Caldwell and Graham Chappell for helping me produce a published book I'm truly delighted with.

Finally, thank YOU for buying this book.

You can find out more about Corrie, Alison and how you are supporting Mary's Meals on the Corrie's Capers website:
www.westie.scot